The House
on the Hill

Retold by Beverley Randell
Illustrated by Ben Spiby

One day, the white sheep said,
"My house is very old.
It is no good.
I will get some wood
and make a new house
up on the hill.
But who will help me?"

"I can help,"
said the grey rabbit.

"No you can't,"
said the white sheep.
"You are too little."

"I'm **not** too little,"
said the grey rabbit.
"I can dig the holes
for the house."

"I can help,"
said the brown duck.

"No you can't,"
said the white sheep.
"You are too little."

"I'm **not** too little,"
said the brown duck.
"I can get some mud
for the walls."

"I can help,"
said the red hen.

"No you can't,"
said the white sheep.
"You are too little."

"I'm **not** too little,"

said the red hen.

"I can fly up

and make the roof."

The grey rabbit
dug the holes.

The white sheep
made the walls.

The brown duck
got the mud.

The red hen

made the roof.

"We have made
a **very** good house," they said.

"Yes," said the sheep.
"Thank you for helping me."

Then they all went inside
the new house on the hill.